Wallace & Gromit™
ANORAKNOPHOBIA

Story and Text by
Tristan Davies
Drawings by
Nick Newman

Hodder & Stoughton

Lettering by Gary Gilbert

Additional colouring by
Tony Trimmer and Fiona Newman

First published in Great Britain in 1998 by Hodder & Stoughton
A division of Hodder Headline PLC

A CIP catalogue record for this title is available from the British Library

ISBN 0 340 74999 7

Printed by Jarrolds Book Printing, Thetford.

Hodder & Stoughton
A division of Hodder Headline PLC
338 Euston Road
London
NW1 3BH

Wallace & Gromit ANORAKNOPHOBIA

WALLACE
Inventor of the ground- (and furniture) breaking Ping-Pong-O-Matic Automated Home Leisure System who, under hypnosis, learns what it's like to lead a dog's life.

GROMIT
A dog already so busy leading a dog's life (washing the socks, ironing the milk cartons, polishing the Tupperware, etc) he has little time for Home Leisure — even if it is Automated.

MR PATEL
Pigeon fancier and expert on prevailing wind conditions, Wallace's nextdoor neighbour is very interested in, er, wind and pigeons.

DEREK
A game old carrier pigeon and Mr Patel's absolutely favouritest bird.

MR DO IT ALL
Doorman, receptionist, porter, bell boy, gardener and barman at the Hotel Splendio on the Northern Riviera.
(It's a job share.)

THE HERR DOKTOR COUNT BARON NAPOLEON VON STRUDEL, *aka* BERT MAUDSLEY
Dastardly founder of the Acme Corporation and inventor of the Acme Utility Anorak, he has a surprise up his sleeve and something even yukkier behind his eye patch.

THE CONTESSA BARONESS MADAME FRAULEIN QUEENIE VON STRUDEL, *aka* QUEENIE MAUDSLEY
Whip-cracking variety artiste whose arachnid trapeze act has mesmerised audiences from Berlin to Barnoldswick — and sometimes all the way back again.

CLEETHORPES and CLITHEROE
Bert and Queenie's polite, erudite twins, whose hobbies are pressing dried flowers and translating the mystical writings of Thomas à Kempis back into Latin.
OR: Two complete and utter nutters. (Delete where applicable.)

DEREK, DERRICK AND ERIC
Gentleman inventors and exhibitionists, who for the purposes of this story are making an exhibition of themselves at an Acme Corporation-sponsored Invention Convention.

THE SPIDERS FROM MARGATE
A troupe of performing arachnids from Margate and the surrounding area (although one, it's true, was brought up by an aunt in Folkestone).

1

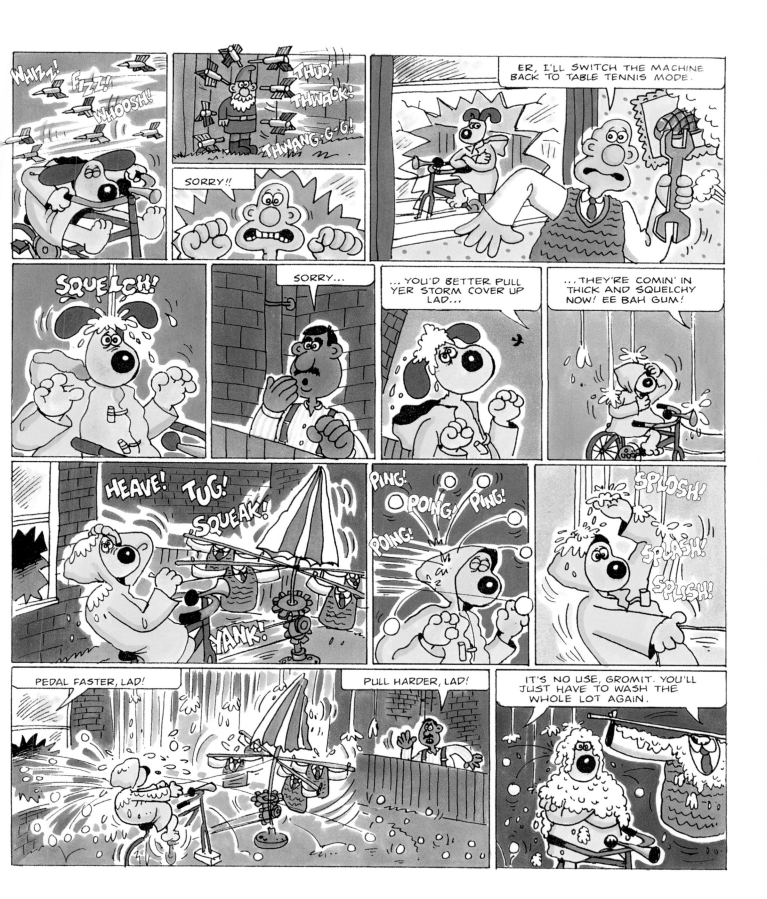

4

6

D-O-O-O SOMETHING, GROMIT! IT'S NOT THE PING PONG-O-MATIC THAT'S MALFUNCTIONING...

... THE VIBRATIONS ARE COMING FROM THE ...

J-JUDDER! — J-JUDDER!

WE EEM OO AV AD A IT O OTHER...

I SAID: WE SEEM TO HAVE HAD A BIT OF BOTHER IN THE LAUNDER-AMA DEPARTMENT.

AND NO WONDER IF THAT'S WHERE ME BILLIARD BALLS WENT.

NOW WE'RE SNOOKERED. WE'LL NEVER REPAIR THIS DRUM -- AND WE CERTAINLY CAN'T AFFORD A REPLACEMENT.

ANY IDEAS, LAD?

FIRST PRIZE £100

TAP! TAP!

SEVERAL HOURS LATER...

THERE. IF WE'RE QUICK WE'LL JUST CATCH THE LAST PIGEON POST.

Acme Corp
P.O. Box 666
England

DEREK!

RUN THIS TO THE POST BOX WILL YOU, CHUCK? APPLICATIONS CLOSE TOMORROW -- AND GROMIT AND ME NEED THE PRIZE MONEY!

PIGEON EXPRESS

8

NOW WE'RE UP THE CREEK WITHOUT A LEG TO STAND ON.

BETTER GET PADDLING.

C'MON LAD. GIVE IT SOME WELLY.

LESS WELLY-GLUG-GLUG-GLUG!

I CAN'T ATTEND THE INVENTION CONVENTION WITH ME TANK TOP COVERED IN SLIME.

SQUELCH! SQUELCH!

HOPE THERE'S TIME TO GET IT LAUNDERED BEFORE I MEET MY FELLOW PIONEERS OF PROGRESS.

ON THE NORTHERN RIVIERA...

TWINNED WITH GRIMSVILLE SUR MER

SLACKEN OFF, LAD. WE'LL FREEWHEEL THE LAST BIT.

HOTEL SPLENDI O ★★

SQUEAK! SQUEAK! SQUEAK!

BLIMEY! THIS LOOKS POSITIVELY, ER, *SPLENDIO*.

OH NO! IT'S THOSE ROAD HOGS AGAIN. REMIND ME TO KEEP THE BATH PLUG IN -- WE DON'T WANT 'EM GETTING IN OUR ENSUITE FACILITIES.

CAUTION LIVE SPIDERS

WELCOME TO THE HOTEL SPLENDIO, SIR -- JEWEL OF THE NORTHERN RIVIERA!

HOTEL

WELC ME

CAN I INTEREST SIR IN OUR PERSONALISED VALET PARKING SERVICE?

NO THANKS. WE TRIED PARKING IN YOUR VALLEY -- AND VERY SQUELCHY IT WAS TOO.

PONG-
O-MATIC
PARTS

BUT I COULD MURDER A WASH AND BRUSH UP!

VERY GOOD, SIR. IF YOU GO TO RECEPTION THE MANAGER WILL SEE YOU SHORTLY.

TWENTY MINUTES LATER...

PRIVATE

INVENTION CONVENTION COCKTAIL PARTY 7.30 IN THE BANQUETING HALL

TWENTY MORE MINUTES LATER...

SERVICE SEEMS A LITTLE ON THE NON-EXISTENT SIDE.

BRRRRING!
BRRRING!

WELCOME TO THE HOTEL SPLENDIO, SIR -- PANT! PANT! -- JEWEL OF THE NORTHERN RIVIERA!

FOR THE COMFORT OF OTHER GUESTS ATTENDING THE INVENTION CONVENTION, WE WOULD ASK YOU TO REFRAIN FROM USING POWER TOOLS IN THE OCEANSIDE BUTTERY RESTAURANT BEFORE 9AM.

AND IN THE MORNING, WILL SIR BE REQUIRING A COMPLIMENTARY...

...NEWSPAPER?

NEWSPAPER!? I HOPE NOT. OUR GROMIT'S HOUSE-TRAINED, YOU KNOW. AND BESIDE'S, WE'VE GOT EN-SUITE FACILITIES.

PRIVATE

PING PONG-
O-MATIC
PARTS

THEN IF YOU'LL JUST FOLLOW ME TO THE LIFT...

PING PONG-
THIS WAY UP
O-MATIC
PARTS

FLIPPIN' 'ECK!!!

PING PONG-
O-MATIC

LOOKS LIKE YOU'LL HAVE TO TAKE THE STAIRS. BUT DON'T WORRY -- IT'S ONLY AN EIGHT-FLOOR WALK-UP!

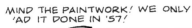

MIND THE PAINTWORK! WE ONLY 'AD IT DONE IN '57!

WILL THAT BE ALL, SIR? AHEM, AHEM!

ER, CAN YOU JUST TELL ME HOW TO CONTACT ROOM SERVICE?

EASY. DIAL 9. FOLLOWED BY THE SUM OF THE TWO DIGITS OF YER ROOM NUMBER. MINUS THE NUMBER OF NIGHTS YOU'RE STAYING. DIVIDED BY WHAT FLOOR YER ON. AHEM AHEM!

ER, HOW D'YOU DO? MY NAME IS WALLACE. PEOPLE CALL ME... WALLACE.

ER, DELIGHTED. WILL THERE BE OWT ELSE?

OO. YOU COULD TAKE ME TANK TOP TO THE LAUNDRY. WE'VE GOT COCKTAILS AT HALF PAST SEVEN AND I WANT TO LOOK ME BEST.

AND ME SHOES AND SOCKS COULD DO WITH A ONCE OVER, AN' ALL.

FORTY WINKS LATER...

COO-COO!
COO-COO!

DON'T PANIC, LAD. IT'S NOT REAL PIGEONS...

ONLY MR PATEL'S COO-COO CLOCK.

NOW WHAT'S HAPPENED TO MY LAUNDRY?

I MUST BE PROPERLY ATTIRED FOR THE CONVENTION. BETTER RING DOWN.

PING PONG
O-MATIC

FUNNY... THE LINE'S DEAD!

14

16

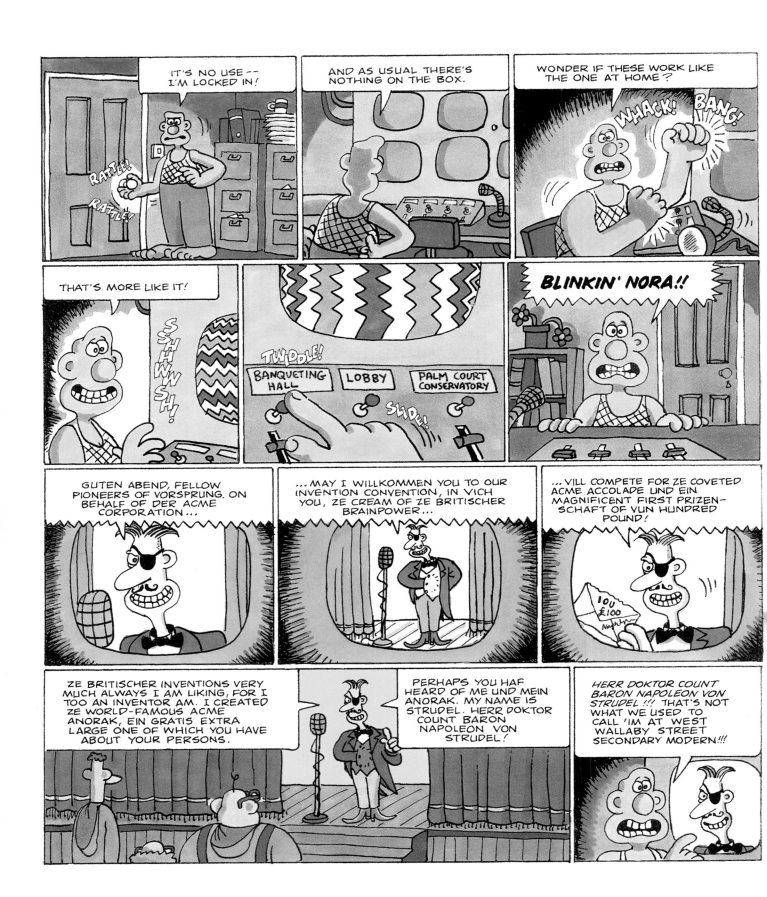

BEFORE VEE ZE INVENTION CONVENTION PROPER BEGINNING ARE...

BACK IN DER BANQUETING HALL...

... EINE KLEINE NACHTMUSIK UND TOP FLIGHT EVENING'S ENTERTAINMENT THE ACME CORPORATION PROPOSING IS.

REMEMBER—VE HAF VAYS OF MAKING YOU ENJOY YOURSELF! AND YOU *VILL* ENJOY ZIS INTERNATIONAL CABARET ARTISTE...

... WHO'S SPELLBOUND AUDIENCES FROM BERLIN TO YOUR OWN DEAR BARNOLDSWICK LADIES UND DAMEN--

THE CONTESSA BARONESS MADAME FRAULEIN ... QUEENIE VON STRUDEL !!!

... UND ZE SPIDERS FROM MARGATE!!!

CANNED APPLAUSE!

WHAT D'YA RECKON, ERIC?

DUNNO, DERRICK. WHAT DOES DEREK THINK?

SHE'S ... A BIG LASS!

KERRACK!

SPIDERS ASCEND -- AND PREPARE TO SPIN!!!

KERRACK!

SPIDERS STEADY -- AND PREPARE TO SWING!!!

BACK IN THE SECURITY ROOM ...

VORSPRUNG DURCH TECHNIK! FORGET THE FLOORSHOW-- THAT'S MY PING PONG-O-MATIC THEY'VE PINCHED!

CLEETHORPES! CLITHEROE!

YES, MAM?

GET THESE THREE ANORAKED -- *NOW!!!*

YES, MAM.

SPIDERS DESCEND *!!!*

AND PREPARE TO WEAVE *!!!*

AS FOR YOU BERT MAUDSLEY...

OPERATION S.P.A.R.R.O.W. CAN'T AFFORD ANY MORE OF YOUR SLIP OOPS!

SO CRANK OOP THE PING PONG-O-MATIC -- AND STICK IT ON DARTS MODE IN CASE THE INVENTORS TRY TO ESCAPE *!!!*

ANYTHING YOU SAY, PET.

CLEETHORPES! CLITHEROE! QUIT SCRAPPIN' *NOW!!!*

IF IT'S A FIGHT YOU WANT, FETCH ME WALLACE -- DEAD OR ALIVE *!!!*

BACK IN THE SECURITY ROOM...

TWIN PIQUES! HERE COMES TROUBLE...

YES, MAM.

AWW! THANKS MAM!

21

'E'S GETTING AWAY! OUR MAM'LL BRAIN US!!

'S ALL RIGHT. I'VE GORRANIDEA. WE'LL GO AFTER 'IM!

FASTER, LAD! THIS INVENTION CONVENTION'S TURNING NASTY. THEY'VE ONLY PURLOINED MY PING PONG-O-MATIC FOR PURPOSES OF A CRIMINAL NATURE!

CRASH! JOLT! JUDDER!

IS THE COAST CLEAR?

CLEARLY NOT! GRAB THAT SERVICE TROLLEY, LAD!

I DON'T KNOW WHAT THE SPEED LIMIT IS IN HOTEL CORRIDORS-- BUT FEEL FREE TO GIVE IT SOME WELLY!!!

HANG ABOUT! LET'S SEE IF WE CAN'T GET THE TWINS INTO A LATHER!

COURTESY BUBBLE BATH

BTTE!

SPTT!

COURTESY BUBBLE BATH

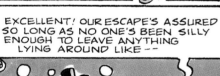

EXCELLENT! OUR ESCAPE'S ASSURED SO LONG AS NO ONE'S BEEN SILLY ENOUGH TO LEAVE ANYTHING LYING AROUND LIKE --

GLUG! GLUG!

A COMPACT VACUUM CLEANER!!!

AAAARRGGHHHH!!!

FIRE POINT

THWACK!

22

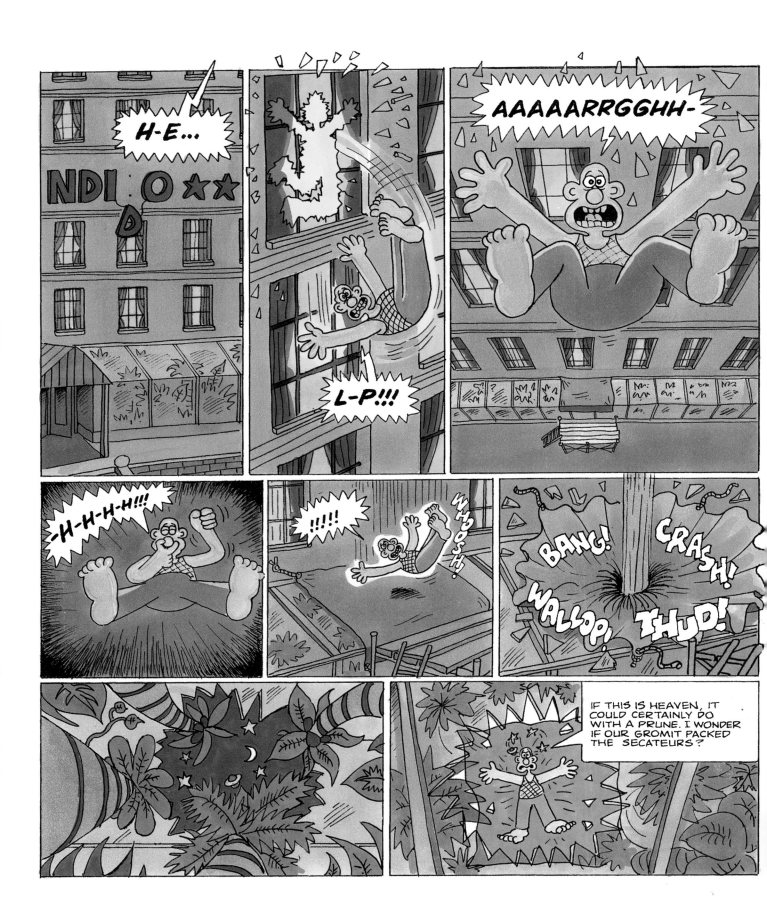

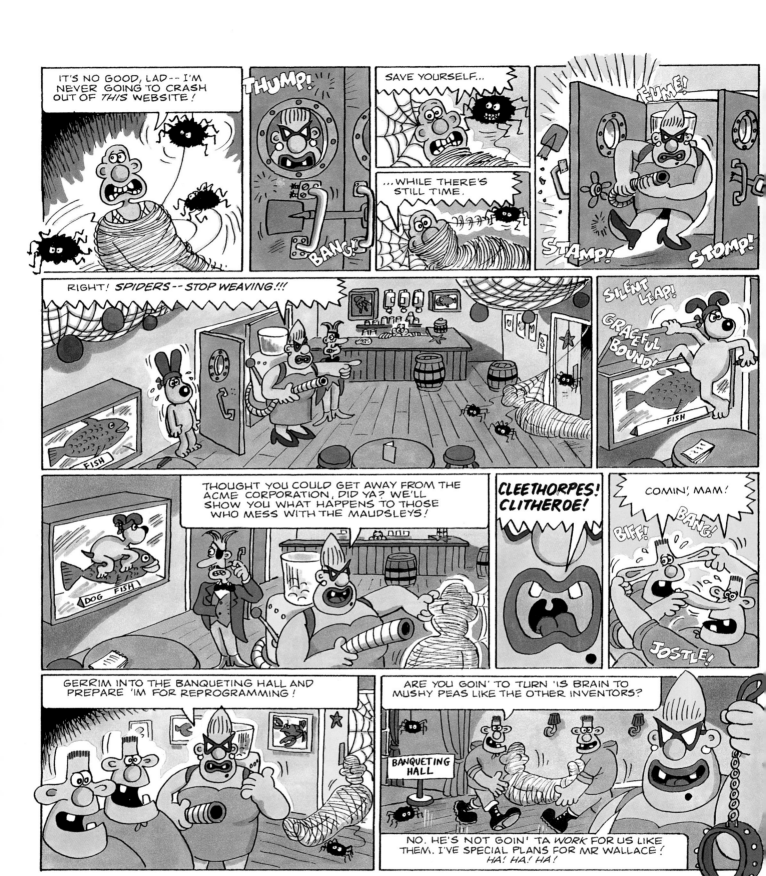

SPIDERS, DESCEND!

NOW WATCH ME HAIRY BEAUTIES, WALLACE. AND LISTEN ONLY TO MY VOICE!

YOU ARE FEELING RELAXED...

...RELAXED AND SLEEPY...

...AS SLEEPY AS THE DOZIEST INVENTOR WHAT WAS EVER INVENTED.'

AND AS YOU CLOSE YOUR EYES, IMAGINE A STEEP STAIRCASE BEFORE YOU.

A STAIRCASE YOU BEGIN TO DESCEND, ONE STEP AFTER ANOTHER.

THAT'S IT. DOWN YOU GO, STEP BY STEP...

LOWER AND LOWER 'TIL YOU REACH THE BOTTOM.

AND AT THE BOTTOM OF THESE IMAGINARY STAIRS YOU SEE WALLACE'S SPECIAL NEW HOME...

SO THAT WHEN I CLICK MY FINGERS...

CLICK!

YOU LEAP INTO YER NEW DOG BASKET !!!

WOOF! WOOF!

HAHAHAHAHAHAHA!!!

WOOF! WOOF!

OW-OWWW!!

MEANWHILE AT SECURITY...
OW-OWWWWW!!

MOAN! WHIMPER!
THUMP! SIGH!

BUT MAM! WHERE'S 'E REALLY GOIN' TO SLEEP? WE 'AVEN'T GOT A KENNEL.

SHUT IT, YOU TWO! HE'LL KIP IN THE CARAVAN WI' US!

GRATEFUL PANT! DRIBBLE!

WALLACE

31

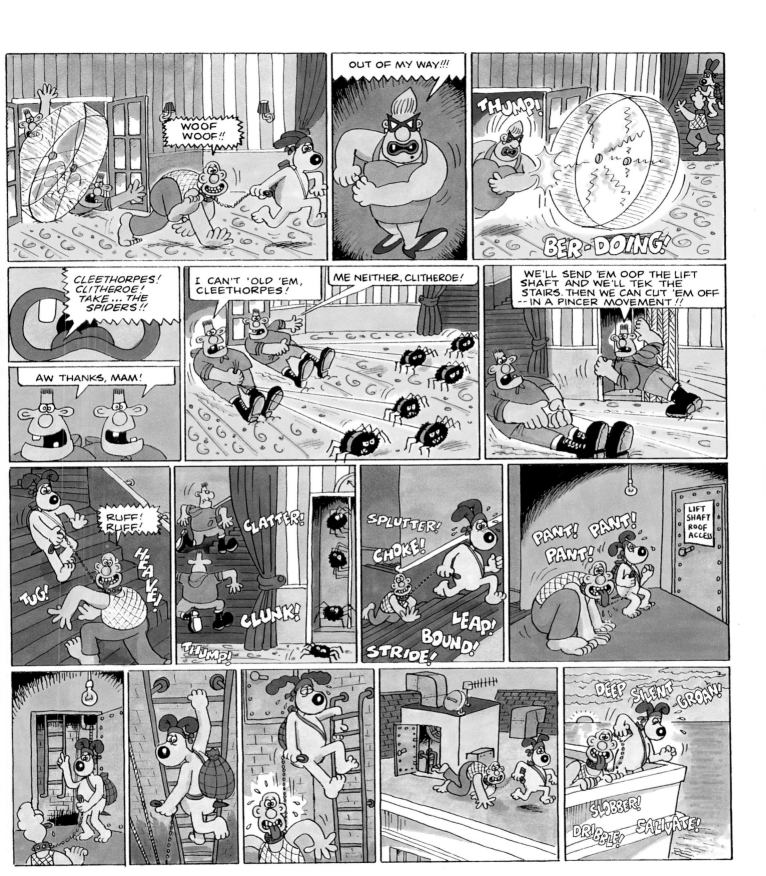

34

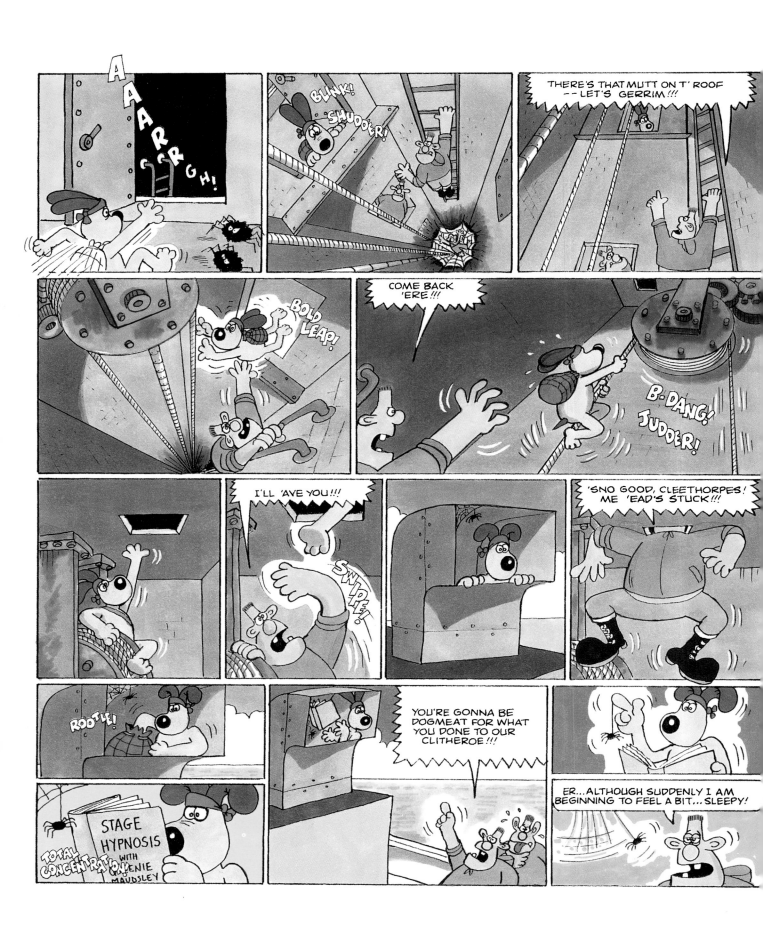

MEANWHILE, INSIDE THE HOTEL SPLENDIO...

HERE HE IS TRUSSED UP LIKE A FERRET AT EASTER!

BUT IT LOOKS LIKE THE TRANCE'S WORN OFF.

WE'LL HAVE TO THINK OF SOMETHING MORE FINAL FOR THE INVENTOR OF THE PING PONG-O-MATIC. BACK TO THE BANQUETING HALL.

RIGHT BERT MAUDSLEY, RUNNER-UP IN THE WEST WALLABY STREET SECONDARY MODERN TABLE TENNIS CHAMPIONSHIPS THREE YEARS RUNNIN'.

SHOW WALLACE WHAT YER MADE OF NOW!

IT'LL BE A PLEASURE, BLOSSOM!

YOU SEE, WALLACE. I'M NOT JUST A PRETTY FACE ALONG WITH THE ACME ANORAK, I'M THE BRAINS BEHIND...

...THE ACME TABLE TENNIS TERROR! THE WORLD'S FIRST SMART PING PONG BALL!

FITTED WITH IT'S OWN HIGHLY UNSTABLE MERCURY SWITCH INERTIA GYROSCOPE LINKED TO A SMALL EXPLOSIVE DEVICE!

READY FOR A MATCH, WALLACE--OR DO YOU ONLY EVER PLAY AGAINST DOGS?

SO THAT'S WHY YOU WANT THE PING PONG -O-MATIC -- TO LAUNCH YOUR EXPLODING SMART BALL. INDOOR LEISURE HAS DONE NOTHING TO DESERVE THIS, BERT MAUDSLEY! YOU'RE EVIL!

SHUT IT, WALLACE! SHOW 'IM WARRELSE YOU'VE GORRUP YER SLEVE, OUR BERT!

YOU MEAN SHOW HIM...

...MY TITANIUM-RIVETED, PLATINUM-PLATED...

...ACME SMART BAT, WHICH IS TUNED TO THE SAME EVIL RADIO FREQUENCY AS THE BALL!

BLINKIN' NORA!

WITH THIS I'M... INVINCIBLE AT PING PONG!

IS THE DEADLIEST SMART BALL ARMED, LAMBKIN?

'TIS NOW, OH MIGHTY ONE!

THEN PLAY! AND REMEMBER: THE BALL EXPLODES INSTANTLY YOU MISS A SHOT...

...IF ITS MAGNETIC MEMORY TOUCHES SO MUCH AS A BLADE OF GRASS ON THE EARTH'S SURFACE.

NOTHING CONCENTRATES THE MIND LIKE PING PONG TO THE DEATH, EH WALLACE?

THE WORLD'S PARIAH TABLE TENNIS COACHES WILL PAY HANDSOMELY FOR THE SMART BALL.

ESPECIALLY WHEN LAUNCHED FROM YOUR OWN RAPID FIRE PING PONG-O-MATIC!

NOTHING IN THE RULES ABOUT NOT OPENING THE WINDOW IS THERE?

YOU BLITHERING IDIOT!!

OH NO!!!

LOOK OUT MISSUS! THERE'S A HIGHLY UNSTABLE TABLE TENNIS TRAINING DEVICE HEADING STRAIGHT FOR YOU!

41

I'D BETTER LOOK FOR DEREK. WIND'S CHANGED AND HE'S BEAK-ON TO AN EASTERLY FORCE 7. GUSTING 8.

YOU CARRY ON: WE'RE ABOUT TO TRY OUT OUR FREE ACME ANORAKS!

NO! PLEEASE! NOT OUR OWN EXTRA LARGE UTILITY GARMENTS! WE BOTH SUFFER FROM...

ANORAKNOPHOBIA!!

DEREK!

YES???

IT'S ERIC, ACTUALLY.

YOU'RE LUCKY MR PATEL BROKE YOUR TRANCE. YOU COULD HAVE BEEN PERMANENTLY BRAINWASHED.

NOW YOU'RE FREE YOU CAN HELP US DEAL WITH THAT LOT.

WE'VE GOT TO CONTACT THE AUTHORITIES BUT THE HOTEL PHONES ARE DEAD.

OH. WE CAN USE THE REVOLUTIONARY NEW INVENTION I ENTERED FOR THE CONVENTION.

THAT'S NOT NEW-- THAT'S A MOBILE PHONE!

AYE. BUT DEREK'S DON'T NEED A BATTERY. IT'S CLOCKWORK...

...AND I'VE INVENTED A MOBILE KEY TO GO WITH IT!

AY UP! DERRICK'S KEY'LL WORK ON MY INVENTION: THE AUTOMATIC CLOCK WINDER THAT WINDS CLOCKS AUTOMATICALLY. ONCE YOU'VE WOUND IT UP, THAT IS. LET'S TRY.

WIND HERE

KEEP WINDING, DERRICK.

KEEP YER HAIR ON, DEREK.

WHIZZ! WHIRR! HOO-LAP! SPIN!

IF THE CONVENTION HAD GONE AHEAD, MY PING PONG -O-MATIC MIGHT HAVE HAD A CHANCE!

43

44